SILENT VALLEY REVISITED

Vic Hallam

BENEATH THE WATERS OF Ladybower Dam lie two lost villages, Derwent and Ashopton. Until the 1940s they were living communities, men, women and children, whose families had lived in the valley for generations. But cities were thirsty for water, and the river that flowed through both villages – the Derwent – had plenty. New dams had been built in the late nineteenth century, north of Sheffield and east of Manchester. Flooding local valleys for water storage was well known.

The River Derwent rises in North Derbyshire on Howden Moors, collecting its first water from the southern Pennines, and flows down the Derwent Valley through the Peak National Park to join the River Tr... south-east of Derby, supplying wa... than two million people as it flows so... 1974 it was administered by the Derw... Water Board, nowadays part of the p... Severn Trent Water Ltd.

The Derwent Valley Water Boar... formed by the Derwent Valley Water Act of 1899, and had for more than seventy years supplied water to Derby, Nottingham, Leicester and Sheffield, and to smaller districts in Derbyshire. Demand for water, for both industrial and domestic use, had grown in the nineteenth century, as the importance of steam power and public health were recognised in towns and cities.

First published in 2002
by Sheaf Publishing Ltd,
191 Upper Allen Street,
Sheffield S3 7GW

ISBN 1 85048 017 6

Looking north up the Derwent Valley in 1946, as Ladybower Dam fills with water for the first time. All but the spire of Derwent church is already underwater, whilst the water rises relentlessly to surround the empty vicarage. A village is lost, forever.

The 1899 Act provided that a Board should be formed consisting of 13 members to be appointed annually. Three would represent Derby Corporation, with four from Leicester Corporation, two from Nottingham, three from Sheffield and just one from the Derbyshire County Council.

To enable it to reserve and supply water, the Board was given Parliamentary powers to construct six impounding reservoirs. These were the Ronksley Reservoir – this to be formed by means of a dam across the River Derwent – Howden and Derwent Reservoirs – again damming the River Derwent – the Hagglee and Ashopton Reservoirs, both to be formed by dams across the River Ashop. To supply water to Sheffield, the plan also included a sixth reservoir, at Bamford, shown at that time to be sited 63 chains or thereabouts measured in a south-south-easterly direction from the centre of the bridge crossing the River Derwent at Bamford, known as Yorkshire Bridge. Also authorised by the Act was a filtration plant at Bamford, various aqueducts and road diversions. It was a mighty plan, which would transform the quiet northern reaches of the agricultural Upper Derwent Valley.

The first instalment of the Act was the construction of the Howden (built between 1901 and 1912) and Derwent (started in 1902 but not brought into use until 1916) Dams in the Upper Derwent Valley, These were built by

Over the course of fifty years the Upper Derwent Valley in Derbyshire was transformed by the building of three dams on the Rivers Derwent and Ashop. Here we see Derwent Village before the waters – the vicarage in the background behind the church, and the village school in the foreground, probably in the 1920s.

'direct labour' – under the supervision of the newly appointed engineer, Mr Edward Sandeman M.Inst.CE, on a salary of £1,200 a year. When you consider the medical officer's salary was £150 per annum, it was a very handsome salary, but one he would earn over the ensuing years.

Mr Sandeman came from Plymouth, with an excellent reputation, having just completed the Burrator Dam. After studying the planned work, he recommended certain changes, including moving the site location of Derwent dam wall some 800 yards up the valley and increasing its height from 89 feet to 114 feet. This increased water capacity allowed the Water Board to remove the Ronksley Dam from their plans, but still retained the high gravitational feed lines out of the valley to the filtration plant at Bamford. This, with other changes, formed part of the Derwent Valley Water Act of 1901.

The Derwent Valley Water Board then began building the Derwent and Howden Dams, the aqueducts, an underground reservoir at Ambergate and a filtration plant at Bamford.

Over the following fifty years the Derwent Valley was to be transformed.

The narrow Derwent Valley combined with the high rainfall of the Peak District made the area ideal for dam building. Howden Dam was the first to be built and is now an accepted part of the landscape though, in recent years, the planting of so many evergreens has been questioned.

Looking west over Howden Dam in 1908 as construction is well underway. Huge pieces of stone were hauled up the valley on a specially built railway line, seen here to the bottom left of the picture, then moved into place using steam cranes and an overhead cableway. Fitting shops and engine sheds stand in the background.

Howden and Derwent Dams

HOWDEN DAM is the highest and most northerly of the dams in the Upper Derwent Valley, and was the first to be built. Work started on the construction in May 1901.

Derwent Dam followed in 1902, when six men armed with picks, roped to a railway girder, began the arduous task of excavating the foundation's trenches. They were later joined by several hundred more men and a little mechanisation, to take down the main foundation trench to a maximum depth of 68 feet below the river bed. This was far deeper than had been first planned, for geologists had reported that a maximum depth of between 30 to 40 feet would be acceptable. The increased depth sought to allow for certain unstable ground, traces of which were apparent along the river bed which, although at first thought to

Local farmers turn out for sheep dipping in the River Derwent around 1887. In the background is Howden House. Within twenty years life in the idyllic Derwent Valley would have changed forever.

be only surface movements, were proved by early excavations to be far deeper than first anticipated.

First calculations had estimated that to complete the works by 1910 a quarry output of 140,000 tons of stone annually would be needed, but with the greater depth this figure increased to 180,000 tons, requiring extra plant, and more labour at the quarry site. This the Board refused to accept, so the Act was amended to allow more time for the project. Mr Sandeman also called for a second opinion as to the stability of the design of the Howden Dam.

Professor Unwin – a design expert from Windermere – submitted a report, recommending certain areas of the Dam that needed strengthening, including the base of towers, and on 23 September 1902 the Engineer held a conference together with the Consulting Engineers. Agreement was reached as to the safety of the Howden Dam, the revised design was approved by the Water Board, and used as a blueprint for the Derwent Dam.

Derwent village in its rural setting as it was before the waters.

As the project would now require some 1.25 million tons of Derbyshire gritstone, the Water Board searched for possible sites to establish a quarry. Much of the stone could have been obtained in the Derwent Valley itself (which at that time was not lined with trees), but the Board felt that the landscape might never recover from the ravages of supplying stone as well as dam building. A site was finally chosen just above Grindleford, known locally as the Bole Hills, which held more than enough stone, and was close by the Midland Railway Company's main line between Sheffield and Manchester for transport to Bamford.

The land was quickly purchased from its owner, Colonel Shuttleworth, in December 1901 and the Water Board appointed Mr J. Welton from Torpantau, South Wales, as Quarry Foreman on an annual salary of £5.5s.0d. plus a cottage.

The Board paid for two purpose-built railway sidings, one at Grindleford Station costing of £1,578 and another at Bamford known as Waterworks Sidings costing £1,828. From Bamford the Board constructed its own $8\frac{1}{2}$ mile standard gauge railway up to the dam sites, to transport the main stone and materials needed for the construction.

Walter Scott and Middleton were given the contract for the railway, which took 18 months to complete. Under the original draft plan each member Corporation of the Water Board was asked to submit a price for the railway. Leicester Corporation came up with a workable quote at a cost of £3,000, yet further investigation showed they had failed to allow for any river crossings – the trestle gantries alone cost £3,000 – and the final cost of the railway was £15,000. (So if you are thinking of building a railway and someone from Leicester estimates for it, check it very carefully!)

By August 1902, the engineer reported that the line had been laid as far as Fairholmes (now a picnic and car-parking site) which was close to the stonemason's yard, five miles from Bamford sidings. Two hundred and forty men were employed on the railway at that time, and 10 horses were said to be working hard and giving satisfaction. Four signal boxes were built in the Derwent Valley by the Midland Railway Company at a cost of £2,800, one each at the Howden and Derwent Dam sites, another at the Fairholmes branch and one at Jack End Farm, which now lies in ruins beneath Ladybower, close to the Ashopton Viaduct.

Most of the stone blocks for the dams were quarried at Bole Hill, near Grindleford. It came by train via Grindleford then to Bamford, on the Water Board's private railway line to the Derwent and Howden sites. At Bole Hill quarry was this spectacular incline, down which a loaded wagon descends (assisted by ropes). The quarry was in use from 1903 to 1910.

A request by the agent of the Duke of Norfolk was granted for a small siding to be built close to Derwent Hall, his country seat. This was to be used by the Hall as a coal dump; when all the fires were lit in the Hall they burned one ton of coal each week.

By 19 May 1903, workshops had been completed at Howden Dam. These housed fitters, blacksmith and joiners fully equipped with steam hammers, drills and lathes. By 1908 the Water Board had 11 steam locomotives working on on the project namely *Bobs, Buller, Dreadnought, French, Kitchener, McDonald* (all 0-4-0 saddle tanks), *King* and *Queen* were 0-6-0 Pecketts as were *Kuroki, Nogi* and *Togo. King* ended his days in a Brazilian scrap yard in 1959 after many years of excellent service.

As well as trains bringing stone, coal for the steam machinery, timber etc, a passenger train – known as the Paddy Mail – left Bamford sidings at 5.15 am taking local workmen up to the dam sites for their working day which commenced at 6.00 am and finished at 5.30 pm, at which time the Mail returned from Howden for Bamford. A second train departed from Bamford at around 9.00 am taking engineers and staff up to the sites.

In 1903 it was agreed by the Water Board to run trains for the use of the people of Birchinlee who needed to journey to Bamford or further afield, and for this purpose a second-hand passenger carriage was purchased, and a regular service started.

The daily 'paddy mail' arrives at Derwent carrying workmen ready to commence their days work on the dam sites. This train left Bamford at 5.15 am. A second, for engineers and staff, left at 9 am. The return run left for Bamford at 5.30 pm.

The Howden and Derwent Reservoirs are of similar design, being formed by masonry dams, each some 178 ft thick at the base, tapering upwards to 10 ft thick at the overflow crest (the top of the dam wall), with a total capacity of 4,100 million gallons of water. The main mass of the Dams is made up of random gritstone blocks (weighing an average six tons) set in concrete, these being washed to help adhesion The water and air side faces are of dressed stone, each numbered as it left the Fairholmes stonemason's yard.

To haul the blocks into place, Smith's steam cranes were used on site, assisted by overhead 'Boldin' cableways, (the anchor points of which can still be seen clearly today). Some problems occurred in the early days with blocks slipping from the grabs and this was overcome by using a locking type grab, designed by the fitters at Howden. One stonemason working on the Derwent site told of an accident in which a friend was killed. As a block was being lowered into place, it slipped, and as it hit the wall, something purple flew past his head. His friend lay beneath the block and his heart was found later 100 yards up the site. Another life gone, but waiting to take his place were many more, as gangs of men arrived daily looking for work.

Other problems arose as the wall progressed. One which was not apparent at the outset was the sealing of the wall ends, and such was the problem that wing trenches had to be cut into the hillsides at either end of both dam walls, these being some 6 ft wide and 200 ft long. These

By 1908 the Derwent Valley Water Board had eleven steam locomotives working on the dam building project, including (from top) Kitchener, French *and* Nogi.

foot of stone could stand 20 tons of crushing power, thus confirming it as ideal for the building of the main body of the dam.

The Yoredale stone, which would be found on the foundation floor of the valley, was an excellent platform on which to build dams, but of no use for the construction of the walls.

The design for the elevation and towers on the project were submitted by William Flockhart, of New Bond Street, London. These were converted into models inspected by the Board, which on 21 February 1905 approved and adopted the designs for both the Howden and Derwent Dams. Mr Flockhart was paid 50 guineas for his trouble.

Work was progressing very well on all fronts and in June 1907 a little piece of history was placed on both dams, when the Record or Memorial stones were 'laid', placed over the doorways at the base of the Derwent and Howden West Towers. At Howden the stone bears the dates 1901–12, but at Derwent only 1902, for it was not brought into use until 1916, and by then thoughts were of War.

Howden, after the outlet valves were closed in January 1912 was overflowing by the time of its formal opening on 5 September 1912.

It had been hoped that the then King George V would be present to perform the opening, but as he was laid low with peritonitis, Sir Edward Fraser, Chairman of the Board undertook the job. Asked what he would like to be presented with to mark the occasion he chose a silver replica of the Dam on an oak base. This was made in Sheffield for £47.16s.3d.

Deep down in the depths of a Howden foundation wing trench in 1907. Health and safety as we know it today was a long way off, but the welfare of the workforce was a high priority on the dam site.

Derwent Dam in 1906. The crane piers show how the stone blocks (plums) were hauled to the body of the dam. Each weighed on average 6 tons. The dam workers' 'doss house' can be seen on the hillside in the background. To the left is Hollingcroft Farm, and on the extreme left, Hancock's Farm.

Howden Dam in 1906. The engineering and fitting workshops stand to the left, as does Marebottom Cottage, later to become the dam keeper's home. The large building on the right was used for storage of cement. Heavy machinery and blocks of stone and concrete were moved about by a combination of steam-powered wagons, cranes and an overhead cableway.

The Derwent and Howden Dam record stones were laid on 21 June, 1907. Here Thomas Gainsford, chairman of the Derwent Valley Water Board, is watched by a large crowd of dam workers and their families as he lays the stone at Howden.

Howden Dam – Febry – 1909

Abbey Farm in 1909, with Howden Dam in the background. The ruins of this building can be seen in times of drought.

At the opening, his deputy was presented with the cast-iron valve wheel worth 2d. and told it would be suitably inscribed later. How true is the old adage, 'You get nothing for being second.'

A marquee was hired, complete with silk drapes, to house the hundreds of invited guests, who enjoyed a luncheon followed by the usual speeches before departing by train fortified with large brandies, happy in the knowledge that their respective town's water supply would be safe-guarded for years to come.

The boiled ham tea for the workforce and their families cost one shilling per head, instead of the original nine pence as the Derby Board members requested brandy and cigars on the journey home. A sports day, followed by fireworks and a dance in the evening at Birchinlee, ended a wonderful day for all concerned, and rightly so.

Derwent Dam was brought into use on 12 July 1916 with little ceremony. Five Board members attended a luncheon held at the *Yorkshire Bridge Inn*, with on the menu home-made oat cakes, potatoes and bacon, followed by Bakewell Tart. So taken was one of the members that he ordered one to take home.

The record stone sited over the West Tower basement door states only the date when construction began in 1902 – it seems sad that 1916 could not have been added later.

The last outlet valve at Howden Dam was closed in January 1912, to hold back the impounded water in the valley. By the time of the dam's formal opening on 5 September that year, it was already overflowing.

Birchinlee Village, the 'Tin Town' of temporary corrugated iron huts built to house the many workers who came to the Derwent Valley from all over the country to build the dams. By 1910, one thousand people lived in the village.

Birchinlee Village

THROUGHOUT the nineteenth and early twentieth centuries, gangs of workmen employed on public works commonly moved around the country from job to job. Living accommodation would be anything from a barn to a self-constructed hut. Diseases of all kinds often followed. With the building of Birchinlee village, the Derwent Valley Water Board rewrote all the rules and what they achieved there was little short of miraculous.

On a site between Derwent and Howden was built the village of Birchinlee, named after the old farm house nearby. The huts were constructed of wood and corrugated iron sheets, built by the Derwent Valley Water Board for workmen and their families engaged on the construction of the two Dams. Building began in the Summer of 1901. By 1903 more than 600 people were living there, and this figure had increased to 901 by October 1910.

On the east side of the valley just above the Derwent Dam site, at an area known as Hollins Clough, the Water Board built a 'Doss' house, at a cost of £947.7s.6d. This acted as temporary accommodation and a screening house for men who arrived seeking employment on the dams project.

Rules for the doss-house were very strict and the Water Board appointed Mr T. Heathcote, an ex-army Sergeant as 'Doss House-keeper' in February 1903.

To obtain entry to this temporary accommodation, the rules obliged applicants to consent to having their clothes disinfected. They themselves had to take a bath. One night's stay cost 6d., entitling them to a clean night-shirt, bed clothes and the use of a common fire for cooking.

If work was obtained the next day, they would then remain in the doss-house for a further week, after which time, if issued with a ticket from the Doss House-keeper, they could then move into the main village to huts set aside for workmen, or into married quarters, where they dwelt with wives and families. A police station with two cells was also built in Birchinlee, but as customers were few, it was later converted into a married quarters hut with just one room reserved for custodial purposes.

By late 1902 the school at Birchinlee opened. Its first headmaster was a Mr A.C. Pritchard

Birchinlee School opened in 1902 and not only educated the children of the village – evening classes helped some workman with reading and writing. The school closed in 1914.

Birchinlee village, with Howden Dam in the background to the right of the picture. In the foreground is a railway gantry, part of the Water Board's private railway system used to transport men and materials to and from the dam sites.

Birchinlee even had its own hospital, which in later years became one of the best hospitals in the area – patients were sent there for treatment from nearby towns .

who, along with his wife, and two assistants took charge of 110 children who attended school on that opening day. Evening classes were also started to assist any workmen and their families with reading and writing.

Health was given priority in the village. In later years Birchinlee was home to one of the best hospitals in the area, and Chapel-en-le-Frith Health Board paid to send patients there. For 2s.3d. one could have anything added or removed and all manner of ailments were treated at Birchinlee. As early as Autumn of 1901, the Water Board considered appointing a medical officer and on the 25 February 1902, the Board received a letter from a Dr Lander of Hathersage stating:

Dear Sirs,
I wish to know if the DVWB will be responsible for the medical attendance on their workmen at Birchinlee village until you appoint your own medical officer. Up to the present time, I have attended several men on different occasions during the last six months or so, and I am now attending a man with inflammation of the lungs, and as yet, I have received no remuneration whatsoever from the men.

Taking the weather into consideration, the shocking state of the roads and having my traps broken down twice, and getting nothing for it, as well as loss of time, the matter has been a dead loss to me.

In future, unless the Water Board will see its way to be responsible, I shall feel compelled to refuse attendance at Birchinlee.
Believe me,
Yours sincerely,
H. W. Graham Lander, MB, CM

By the spring of 1902 the Board had appointed its own full-time Medical Officer,

Charles Harcourt on a salary of £150 per annum, a position he held until 14 August 1906, when the Water Board accepted his resignation.

The spiritual needs of the people of Birchinlee were also provided for by Walter Rouse, the Vicar of Derwent, who was appointed Chaplain of Birchinlee. For his once weekly service, he was paid £70 per annum.

By the spring of 1902, Mr Eustace Sutton had taken up the post of Missioner to Birchinlee. This fine hard-working man was paid £80 per annum, a salary which never reflected the tremendous job he did in the village.

When the 'Grim Reaper' visited Birchinlee, it was to the village of Derwent, just down the valley, that people took that last journey to their final resting place in Derwent Churchyard. (All bodies interred at Derwent were later removed to private graves in the High Peak or to the special plot in Bamford Churchyard in 1943 when Ladybower was being constructed). Ninety-four people from Birchinlee were buried in Derwent Churchyard.

Some were interred in private graves bought at a cost of £14, but most were buried in communal graves on a large plot, sited on the north west side of the graveyard close to the wall, which for years bore neither headstone nor markers. However, this matter was put to rights by the Water Board when a Memorial Cross was erected at Derwent Church. Carved out of Aberdeen granite, it bore the inscription: *'Erected by the DVWB workmen and friends to the memory of those women and children of Birchinlee and all the men employed on the construction of the Derwent and Howden Reservoirs who died 1901–1912'.*

The cost of £82.3s.6d. was split between the Water Board, workers and friends. This cross now stands in Bamford Churchyard.

Eustace Sutton worked very closely with the Vicar of Derwent and his contribution did much to help the uneasy relationship between the Valley people and the dam-builders. He also recorded many useful insights into the life of Birchinlee. One, written in 1914, recalled his arrival in 1902. According to Mr Sutton the area was up to the boot tops in mud, and it seemed to have rained for days. After arriving in Bamford at 9 am he was taken to Derwent to meet the Vicar. He also spoke highly of the kindness shown to him and his family by Edward Sandeman and it appears the two held great respect for each other during the ensuing years.

On arriving at Birchinlee with Walter Rouse, he was introduced to a few workmen who downed tools and greeted him with great joy, one

Waiting for the Derwent Canteen to open – the only place licensed to sell alcohol in Birchinlee village. It only sold beer – spirits were supplied by the doctor for medical use only.

The main street in Birchinlee. The sweet shop on the right did a good trade with the children of the village.

Sport was a popular pastime for the residents of Birchinlee. Their football team played in the Sheffield Amateur League and was a force to be reckoned with locally.

with the words, 'Hello chum, what brings you to this hole?' As no provision shops were open, he was given all his family's needs by his new neighbours, all of whom he would be meeting for the first time. At that time only 40 huts had been erected; the school, hospitals and recreation hall were still things for the future. The railway was only part made and the work on the dam sites was still at the excavation stage. But this fine man soon joined in the spirit of the Valley and he proved over the years to be one of the Water Board's best appointments.

Sports of all types were very popular and most interests were catered for. Field sports were usually held on the area in the front of Howden Dam site, known as the Abbey Field, named after Abbey Farm which stood close by.

The Water Board paid £50 towards the cost of a mower and roller for the cricket club, and one annual fixture was against the Water Board members themselves, a fine light-hearted affair, which the 'Bosses' usually won. Not so the local 'Battle' against Derwent, of which one witness said they were mostly ill-tempered matches, not really cricket, but perhaps that is understandable.

On the football field, Birchinlee were really a top force, joining the Sheffield Amateur League, and many a splendid match was held on the Abbey Field. One was the local derby with Hathersage, a team in the same league. Glory came to Birchinlee in 1912 when the first team won two cups and three sets of medals.

Many of the men held an allotment in which some grew prize-winning flowers and vegetables. Judged each year at the village show and with good prize money at stake, the best-kept allotment prize was highly sought after.

Indoor sports were held in the recreation hall. Built in 1902, it housed two fine billiard tables, a

Christmas at Birchinlee. Family and friends gather round for lunch. Note the range and open fire on the right of the picture, on which the lady of the house cooked all the meals.

Christmas Cheer.

very popular pastime nationwide at that time. (In 1912 the tables were sold to Bamford Institute, where they still give excellent service today). A stage was also built in the hall, from where many shows were put on, ensuring full houses, with visitors journeying from far and wide. Whilst drives, dances and pantomimes were all staged over the years at Birchinlee.

As shops became available the Water Board had plenty of takers, though rents varied. A grocer's shop was let to Gregory Bros. for £60 per annum in March 1902, an a draper's shop to J. Morris for £35 per annum. A tailor's shop was let to Harry Oliver for an annual rent of £25, whilst a shoemaker's shop was let to Knowles Bros. and Daniel for only 19s.4d. per annum.

Life was hard at first for this isolated community, something not uncommon at the time, yet soon it proved just what could be achieved by people joining together for a common cause.

But when the job was finished, the families and men would go their own way and the village of Birchinlee declined from late 1912 until it was no more by 1916.

Many proposals for its future use were discussed, ranging from an Isolation Hospital to a Prison, but none was taken up and Birchinlee was systematically dismantled and sold off. Traces of the villages can be found today, foundations of huts etc, but these are on private land. The old red brick incinerator used by the village still stands close to the road, on the west side below Howden Dam, providing a memorial to the village in the Valley and its people. Parts of the railway line (though without tracks) can still be followed.

Today, only a granite cross in a churchyard, two stone dam walls and four towers in a Silent Valley bear witness to almost fifteen years activity by hundreds of people.

The site of the future Ladybower Dam wall, pictured in late 1934. A trial borehole can be seen in the centre-left of the picture, and a toilet block is in place in the foreground. The farm in Parkin's Field was the home of the Wilson family.

Ladybower Dam

BY THE DERWENT VALLEY WATER ACT of 1920, the Derwent Valley Water Board obtained Parliamentary powers to abandon the reservoirs authorised by the 1899 Act but not yet built. As it had earlier bought Derwent Hall and certain lands from the Duke of Norfolk's estate, the Board was now able to plan to replace the proposed Bamford Dam with a new construction, the giant Ladybower Dam.

The planned location for the new dam wall was moved north, to a better site, just above Yorkshire Bridge. In 1934, Derby and Leicester Corporations each gave notice to the Board that they required more water, so it was decided to proceed with the construction of Ladybower Reservoir, which when filled would have a surface area of 504 acres, a perimeter of 13 miles, and a maximum depth of 135 feet. At that time the plans made Ladybower the largest artificial reservoir formed by the construction of an earthwork embankment in Europe.

For geological and other reasons Ladybower Dam is totally different both in appearance and structure from those of the Howden and Derwent. It consists of an earthwork embankment with a clay core.

A foundation trench was taken down to an average depth of 182 feet and maximum depth of 225 feet, and filled with concrete to prevent water finding its way through the natural ground beneath the embankment. When the Ladybower is full, instead of flowing over the crest of the dam, as it does with the Derwent and Howden dams, here the surplus water is carried away by two funnel shaped overflows each

80 feet in diameter, carrying the overflow water beneath the embankment, through tunnels 15 feet in diameter and discharging then into in the tail-bays and from there to the River Derwent.

The length of the Ladybower embankment is 1,250 feet, its greatest thickness 655 feet, tapering to 17 feet at the top. At the outset the planned storage capacity of the reservoir was 6,300 million gallons. A pumping plant was installed and the planned daily quantity of water available to the Water Board was 53,666,000 gallons, of which 37,000,000 gallons were available for supplying the four corporations and Derbyshire local authorities. 100,000 tons of concrete, 1,000,000 tons of earth and 100,000 tons of clay were used on the construction of the trench and embankment alone, this being obtained from land between Bamford and Hope, close to the *Rising Sun Hotel*. Carried to Bamford by the LMS railway, from there it was taken to

The small settlement of Ladybower, which was known as 'Chilbage' in earlier times, at the junction of the Sheffield and Bamford Roads.

The Ladybower Inn *replaced an earlier inn which stood 50 yards up the road looking towards Sheffield. Its ruins can still be traced.*

the dam site on the Board's own standard gauge railway, re-opened approximately over the same route as used for the earlier Howden and Derwent Dam building.

A large amount of stone was also needed for 'Beaching' and 'Pitching' the water side of the wall, and for this the Water Board established a quarry at Ladybower (close by the present Inn). Other stone was brought from Millstone Edge, near Hathersage, and Rowsley, much of which arrived by road transport, which, by the 1930s, was much improved.

After the first works had been built by direct labour, it was decided to contract-out the Ladybower project. The contract was won by R. Baillie, a Scottish firm from East Lothian, with Messrs G.H. Hill and Sons of Manchester as the chosen designer. The contract also provided for all unskilled labour to be recruited through the Sheffield Labour Exchange and the work-force conveyed to and from Sheffield by omnibus at the Water Board's expense.

Construction commenced in May 1935 and carried on throughout the Second World War years in spite of immense problems obtaining labour and materials after 1939. Items which were available increased in price daily and the

Water Board had to reach an agreement with the contractors who had requested a special War Fund compensation to help meet the extra costs.

Many prisoners of war were later put to work on the dam and the Works Foreman spent much time searching for them rather than pursuing his true duties. There were 312 men working on the site when War broke out in 1939; six months later only 218 remained, such were the demands of War upon the adult male population. But whereas their average wage in September 1939 was around £3.8s.10d. (£3.44p), by the following March it had increased to almost £4.0s.0d. In the same period, material costs had arisen by 12.5%, making a compensation payment vital for the contractors.

Once used to the rigours of war, work on the dam and its associated works continued steadily (although it is noteworthy that no work was done between December 1939 and March 1940 due to bad weather). As the reservoir was built across the Sheffield to Glossop Road, and would obliterate the roads north and south of Ashopton, to Derwent and Bamford, the plans required some two miles of new diverted highway from Glossop to Sheffield, a similar length of new road from Ashopton to Derwent and a rather shorter length of new road from Bamford to Ashopton. This entailed the construction of $5\frac{1}{4}$ miles of new roads, and two large viaducts of reinforced concrete carrying these new roads , water mains and cables over arms of the Reservoir at Ashopton.

The water mains consisted of two lines of pipes, 48 inches in diameter, whilst the cables were for the Post Office Telephones (now BT). The viaducts were constructed by Messrs Holloway Brothers, London, Ltd to the designs and under the supervision of Dave Anderson (Westminster) and Mr W.M. Keay (Leicester).

The remainder of the road diversions were carried out by the main contractor, Richard Baillie.

The viaducts were designed by Mr D. Anderson (Westminster) and Mr W.M. Keay (Leicester) and constructed by Messrs. Holloway Brothers, London Ltd. (1938–42). They were constructed of steel truss arch and cantilever sections which are protected by concrete cladding. The timing of construction has had an effect on the deterioration of the structures, shortage of man power and materials due to the War commitments left examples of poor workmanship.

During their lives the viaducts have been subjected to an increase in both traffic volume and weights, notably heavy goods vehicles which are the most damaging, and more recently, the road decks have been sprayed with de-icing salt every winter. Following site investigations, deterioration of the concrete at the viaducts was found to be caused by mechanisms of poor quality concrete and insufficient cover to the steel reinforcement, the steel had corroded causing the concrete to flake off in places. The full extent of the corrosion to the steel reinforcement was not evident until removal of the concrete was taking place. Concrete core and lab tests proved that the concrete was weak due to the high initial water/cement ratio plus additional materials and this caused much of the deterioration.

With the increase in the quantity of water available for supply as a result of bringing Ladybower into use, the Water Board had to increase the capacity of their Filtration Plant and Aqueduct. The conversion of the Slow Sand

One of the funnel-shaped overflow shafts, 80ft in diameter, which carries surplus water through tunnels under Ladybower dam. In 1946, following a flash flood, a number of tools including 21 shovels were found two miles down the River Derwent.

The top picture shows the finishing touches being put to the great earthwork dam that encloses the waters of the Ladybower reservoir. Below is the west overflow shaft. The walkway was removed in 1962 to allow more flow.

Filters at Bamford to rapid gravity was carried out by direct labour to the design and under the supervision of R.W.S. Thompson, Engineer to the Board. This doubled the filtration capacity from 12 million gallons to 24 million gallons per day. A third line of pipes 48 metres in diameter was laid between Derwent Dam and Bamford Filters and old pipelines between Bamford and Sawley were duplicated. This work involved laying 26 miles of pipes, varying in diameter from 39 to 48 inches. The Contractors were Messrs Lehane, Mackenzie & Shand Ltd and G.F. Tomlinson & Sons Ltd, both from Derby.

To provide accommodation for families whose homes had been demolished to make way for Ladybower, the Water Board erected 52 houses and two sales shops (later turned into houses) on an estate at Yorkshire Bridge.

Mr William Keay from Leicester designed the houses and was paid a fee of £625.11s.6d. The builder was Thomas Wilkinson from Sheffield and his final bill came to £46,620.2s.8d. The houses, sited in three rows known as Bemrose, Parsons and Steward Gates, take their names from past Derwent Valley Board Members. The first houses to be let in 1938 were numbers 1 and 2 on Bemrose Gate, to the local Police Constable and Mr John Shayler, the Water Board's Foreman, at a rent of 14s.0d. a week.

On 29 May 1938, the Water Board received a claim for compensation from Mr W. Bennett a local farmer, who had four of his lambs killed on the Board's railways. Though he valued them at £8 each, the Board claimed someone had broken their fence, and paid only £4 in full total.

Despite all the problems and shortages caused by the War, Ladybower was well on its way to completion by the time the Armistice was signed in 1945, and arrangements were well in hand for an Inauguration Ceremony, set for Tuesday 25 September 1945. The then King George VI, and Queen Elizabeth, (the late Queen Mother) accepted the invitation to perform the opening ceremony. This turned out to be a highlight in Peakland history.

Between 1998 and 2000, the Ladybower wall has been raised and strengthened, for continuous monitoring revealed that settlement of the dam wall was too great, failing to meet new standards for reservoir flooding.

Upgrading the Dam to meet modern standards was the core of a £23 million refurbishment for the Ladybower Dam Complex which began in January 1998. Further work is due to be carried out at Bamford water treatment works and on the pipe bridge across the reservoir.

Initially the contract for the refurbishment of the viaducts included the reconstruction of the road decks to satisfy the requirement to carry 40-tonne loads, carry out concrete repairs to the structures, refurbish the bridge bearings to the viaducts and improve Heatherdene Car Park. However, because of the problems with the concrete, Severn Trent Water, who had by then taken over from the previous owners the Derwent Valley Water Board, decided to remove and replace as much of this 'cladding' as possible. Approximately 1500 cubic metres of concrete has been removed from the structures, crushed and re-used either in the construction of the car park or on forestry roads. As part of the work cycleways have been incorporated on the viaducts and the junction of the A57 with Derwent Lane has been improved.

On Thursday 21 September 2000, the Rt Hon Michael Meacher, Minister for the Environment, opened the gates to allow the public access to a newly refurbished Ladybower Dam. The Dam has been strengthened with the addition of 400,000 tonnes of rock from a special quarry on Win Hill. In addition, the dam crest and the A6103 which runs alongside have both been raised. and a new eastern abutment has been built.

Children from Bamford primary school were the first to actually walk across the new dam crest and among the guests were two former dam workers Jack Bullivant, formerly a draughtsman and Fred Sutton. As a result of the improvements, visitors to the Derwent Valley will now be able to walk across the crest of the Ladybower Dam for the first time, enjoying spectacular views. There are now also dedicated cycle ways across the Ashopton and Ladybower viaducts, 18 miles of footpaths and tracks to compliment the Visitor Centre at Fairholmes. All these improvements add another chapter to the history of the Derwent Valley's vital role in providing water supplies for the people of Sheffield and the East Midlands.

Just as in the 1940s, the recent work and apparent ravages of dam-building have caused some people to wonder whether the Valley would ever recover from the Ladybower project. But now as we gaze across this man-made Lakeland, one can be forgiven for forgetting the past, though we must not forget that beneath the water of Ladybower there lie the ruins of two lost Derbyshire villages, Derwent and Ashopton.

King George VI and Queen Elizabeth opening the outlet valve at the Ladybower inauguration ceremony in September 1945 before a crowd of 55,000.

The village of Derwent, with the soon-to-perish Mill Cottage, home of Miss Thorpe, seen here on the right. Running right through the village was the Mill Brook which still feeds into Ladybower Dam. Derwent Post Office was run by Mr Bingham.

Derwent Village

Derwent Village

WITH THE completion of Ladybower reservoir, the gains in water storage were tremendous, but the loss of the beautiful and historic villages of Ashopton and Derwent meant that a high price had been paid.

We can sometimes glorify the past when we have an interest in an area, yet it is easy to overlook the conditions under which people once lived. At times they could be very, very hard. The pace of life was usually set by the seasons, and the loneliness of remote areas must have placed an added strain, particularly on women and their children. Food, although adequate in many ways, did not have the variety of modern times. Death and disease often arrived with a single knock on the door; the journey from the font to the grave was for many a short one. Hours of hard work often bought just enough to eat and little else. But looking back on the old photographs, people seemed to be happy with their lot, and I don't know what the old folks would make of our high-speed world today.

Villagers turned out for this photograph in 1912, many of them in their Sunday best. The Post Office is at the end of the terrace.

Bridge End Farm, standing at the west end of Packhorse Bridge, once held an ale license.

Grainfoot Farm, below, in 1935 the home of the Wain family. The ruins of this building can still be traced today half-a-mile south of the village.

It is easy to let our mind's eye wander and picture areas as they used to be in earlier times. One such place is a small Derbyshire village nestling peacefully in a beautiful valley, with small stone cottages and tree-lined lanes where in spring the smell of blossoms and lilacs draw you to the gates of a Victorian church, stone-built in 1867. From its tower four bells call the village people together. Turning around, one sees a large mansion, its stonework glorious in the pale sunshine, its interior rich with oak-panelled walls, home to art treasures and tapestries dating back to the twelfth century.

From an upstairs window, looking over the south garden with clipped yew trees and flowering borders the River Derwent is crossed by a narrow twin-arched bridge, once used by pack horses.

Alas, now it is just a dream, but well within living memory it was also very real; the village was Derwent, the ancient mansion Derwent Hall.

Between 1943 and 1945 water in the silent Derwent Valley steadily rose. By 1944 the site of the school was already under water, and the church, as Derwent Hall seen here in the background, lay in ruins. Sheep graze where once lived a thriving community.

Derwent Hall and the main gates on the west front.
The early part of the Hall was built in 1672 and this
photograph shows the dated lintel stone over the front
door. This stone was rediscovered in 1989.

Derwent Hall

THE ORIGINAL PART of Derwent Hall was built by Henry Balguy, whose coat of arms and the date 1672 were carved over the main doorway. A similar carving and the date 1674 could be seen over the stable door. Balguy built the Hall for his son and heir, who was due to be married. The land for the site of the Hall was bought from the Wilson family of Broomhead. Three cottages originally stood on the site, known as 'Waterside', and these were demolished, with some of the stone kept to build the Hall. Two cottages were later built on a new site, bearing the name 'Waterside'.

The Balguy family date back to Edward I. Thomas de Balgi married an heiress of the Astons, with a large dowry including lands in Derbyshire and Cheshire. The family contributed sons of distinction in both the law and the church from the reign of Elizabeth I onwards. There were Balguys at Hope, Aston and Rowlee. Henry was an attorney and married three times, gaining considerable wealth from each marriage. His first wife was Grace Barber of Rowlee; the second Elizabeth Allyn of Tideswell; the third Anne Moreword of Dronfield. Henry Balguy kept a private bank by storing his money in an oak chest.

There is a story told of a woman who had a strong desire to inspect his hoard of gold. Henry in gratifying her wish, invited her to help herself to a handful, but the coins were so firmly wedged that she could not remove a single one.

At least three generations of Balguys occupied the Hall, spanning almost 100 years. The family also rebuilt the pack-horse bridge on the site of an earlier bridge built by monks.

Derwent Hall was built by Henry Balguy, and at least three generations of his family lived here. The family also rebuilt the Packhorse Bridge, which crossed the River Derwent, opposite where Bridge End Car Park is now sited. The bridge was rebuilt at Slippery Stones, $1^1/_4$ miles above the head of Howden Dam.
The east front of Derwent Hall gave onto an ornamental garden of Irish yews.

In the chancel of Hope Church, a small brass plate may be seen, commemorating Henry Balguy, who died in March 1685 after – we assume – a very full life.

After the Balguys, the Hall at Derwent passed through various hands, and a variety of states of repair, until in 1831 it was sold to a John Read, formerly of Norton Hall, to the south of Sheffield. Read first furnished three rooms only and used the Hall as his summer seat. In 1833 the lease ran out on Norton Hall, so Mr Read decided to put Derwent Hall in a proper state of repair and make it his home.

In the words of his niece, Mrs M.A. Rawson of Wincobank Hall, 'It had been a nice place to live in former times, but, had latterly been used as a common farmhouse. When I first saw it, its appearance was most desolate and dark, and I thought it would be almost impossible ever to make it a comfortable, habitable abode. My uncle's determination and good taste conquered all difficulties and he made it a really delightful residence.'

Most of the rooms had new floors and windows that had been filled in were again opened up. The bare drab walls were covered, some with oak panels, others with fine tapestries, and all the fireplaces were renovated. A practically new fireplace was fitted in the drawing room, and when the Hall was pulled down this fireplace was one of the most sought-after items. John Read also purchased two thousand acres of moorland and sent invitations to his noble friends to visit him during the shooting season.

The private Roman Catholic chapel, built in the 19th century, stood at the end of Derwent Hall. The ornate 'White Altar' was moved to Our Lady of Sorrows Chapel at Bamford before it was taken to Norfolk in the late 1940s.

He remained single, as did his sister Ann, who made an excellent and charming hostess.

Soon to follow in John Read's footsteps was the Newdigate family, whose pedigree went back to Saxon times. In the middle of the 18th century they held the Manor of Kirk Hallam near Derby. The interior of Derwent Hall again had a facelift. More oak panelling was installed, rare silk curtains were hung in all the bedrooms, and an air of grandeur again returned to the Hall. The Newdigates are also credited with the building of the road from Ashopton to Derwent in 1824.

The road, which lies entirely under what is now the Dam, followed the eastern bank of the river, and at the village it turned sharply to the right, whilst the road to the Hall continued along the river bank to the gates of the park. Just before the gates on the left stood the old pack-horse bridge, which provided the only means of crossing the river from the village. It was the ancient bridle path leading from Derwent to Glossop. In 1866 the Newdigates sold the Hall to the trustees of the Duke of Norfolk, and the building was enlarged and a private chapel added at a cost of £23,000. A Roman Catholic chapel was also built above the village.

In a county directory of 1871, the area of Derwent is shown as 3,190 acres with a population of 187 people, the Woodlands being 19,999 acres, population of 220. The Duke of Norfolk used the Hall mainly as a shooting lodge, and according to many who saw him in the village, walking around in old clothes not really befitting a man of his status, he was said to be a very modest aristocrat. He was a notoriously bad shot. One day whilst out grouse shooting after a morning spent expending shot with no result,

his aide snapped, 'you couldn't hit a flying haystack!'. The Duke turned and quietly said 'I don't think I could' and handed him his gun. That evening, grouse was on the menu and the

The interior of Derwent Hall was decorated extensively with oak panelling, as here in a bedroom, and the library.

Looking east across the River Derwent to Derwent Hall.

Duke was congratulated on his excellent shooting that day. Was the red glow on his face due to wine?

One day the Duke was out walking and climbed over a wall belonging to Grainfoot Farm, only to see the wall collapse beneath him. He presented himself at the farm door, telling the surprised farmer to get it put right and send the bill up to Hall. The wall was rebuilt but no bill was ever sent to the Hall.

From the old Duke, the Hall passed into the hands of Lord Fitzalan who later sold it to the Water Board. On 25 September 1924 it was agreed that the Water Board should look into taking early possession of the Hall without necessarily completing the purchase, after which time the Board agreed to form a Derwent Hall Committee to decide the best use of the Hall

and the disposal of its artefacts. The committee was made up of Alderman Bemrose, chairman of the Board, his deputy, Alderman Parsons, and Alderman Fenton, Board member for Sheffield. On 26 March 1925, an agreement was reached whereby the Board took full possession of Derwent Hall. Lord Fitzalan submitted a letter via Mr Baldwin Young, solicitor acting for the family, with regards to certain items that they wished to retain, notably a pair of large ornamental gates and the bell from the private chapel.

A valuation by Ernest G. Denner and Co. of Sheffield was also submitted with regards to the electric lighting plant and fittings. The board agreed a price of £214.5s. for the plant and fittings, less the amount of fittings retained by Lord Fitzalan and they also agreed to pay the fee of 3 guineas for the original valuation. At the same meeting, it was agreed that the Board should pay £10,000 for the hall, together with certain lands amounting to approximately 120 acres, payment deferred until 1927. But on the 14 January 1926 a letter from Lord Fitzalan's solicitors asked whether the Water Board would now pay the full amount early. This request was quickly withdrawn when the discounted price for early payment was returned by the Board.

As the committee searched for the best way forward, two offers of £2,600 and £3,250 respectively were received from Joseph Oxley of Sheffield and C. Gustave of Manchester for dismantling of Derwent Hall and removing of all materials. These were dismissed as totally inadequate. By late November 1927, the Water Board paid the £10,000 for Derwent Hall in full and £210 conveyance fee for the transfer.

It was now agreed by the Derwent Hall committee that it was most urgent to find someone to take the hall on a long lease, as they had no immediate plans for the site, but over the next five years little progress was made. Items from the interior were sold off, including panelling from the library and boudoir and a door from the smoke room for £197, plus a carved oak door from the drawing room for £12, sold to Mr G.M. Eaton, an architect from Derby.

One proposal nearly came to fruition when members of the convalescent and after-care committee of the joint Sheffield Hospitals inspected the hall with a view to leasing it. Mr R. Mathews, chairman of the Royal Infirmary and Mr F. Osbourn chairman of the Royal Hospital together with Mr C.W. Cuff, one of Sheffield's best known surgeons, attended several meetings but finally decided not to take up the lease, as an agreement could not be reached as to who should pay for most of the repairs. These might have been considerable, for dry rot was evident in certain rooms.

The Board then continued their strip and sell policy. On 8 January 1932, just as the Board were about to place an advertisement in newspapers published in four towns inviting offers of a lease on the hall for a period of 10 years, a letter arrived from the Derby secretary of the Youth Hostels Association stating their proposals for leasing the hall. A meeting was hurriedly arranged to try and reach an agreement to suit both parties. On 17 February 1932 the Water Board met a deputation from the YHA, where their secretary, Mr Ramsbottom, explained at length the plans of the Association together with their proposals for the Hall. Only a few outstanding points remained and it was agreed to lease certain parts of the Hall and gardens at a rental of £50 per annum plus all taxes and rates that may be payable. It was also later agreed to allow them the use of the smoke room

and entrance hall plus a small part of the south terrace and a field, the areas to be barricaded by the YHA to the entire satisfaction of the board's engineer. The rent was then increased to £52.19s. per annum and the common seal was affixed to the agreement on 28 July 1932.

As the number of daytime visitors to the Hall grew, the honorary secretary of the Youth Hostels Association, North Midlands Region, wrote to the Water Board asking for permission to announce that visitors could only be shown over the old Hall between the hours of 10 am and 5 pm, at a charge of sixpence, which would be divided equally between the Hostel and the Wardens. This proposal was agreed.

Derwent Hall was opened as a Youth Hostel in 1932 by the Prince of Wales, who went on to become the abdicating King Edward VIII. Scouts formed a Guard of Honour. Over the following years hundreds of people stayed at the old Hall.

Report to Board Meeting 30 November 1933 by Derwent Hall Committee

Ash Tree House
218 Osmaston Road, Derby
23 November 1933

To the Members of the Board
Gentlemen,
Derwent Hall
Some little time back I was informed by the Clerk that the Sheffield Allotments and Social Centres for the Unemployed wished to use the grounds and premises at Derwent Hall, not merely as a Summer Camp, but would like to continue their work there, in some form or other, during the Winter months.

Mr Steward also told me that there were certain matters which had been discussed between the representatives of the Youth Hostels Association and the Sheffield 'Unemployed' Committee, and had been agreed between them, but which required to be considered by the Board, who would have to approve various re-arrangements connected with those matters.

It was hoped that the Members of Derwent Hall Committee would meet representatives of the Youth Hostels Association and the Sheffield 'Unemployed' Committee at the Hall and discuss with them the various proposals, but this was found impossible. However, as Sir John Bell and I had to go to Bamford for a Sealing Meeting on 20 October, we agreed to visit the Hall on that day and, at the suggestion of the Clerk, we asked Alderman Blanchard and Alderman Thraves to join us. On the 20 October, then, Sir John Bell, Alderman Blanchard, Alderman Thraves and I, with the Clerk and the Engineer, met at Derwent Hall Mr L. Ramsbottom and Miss D.M. Wood, representing the Youth Hostels Association, and Mr F.M. Osborn and Mr D.G. Jones, representing the

Sheffield Allotments and Social Centres for the Unemployed.

We made a thorough inspection of the Hall and the outbuildings and also the gardens and the land used by the 'Unemployed' Committee, commencing with the gardens, where the scheme of cultivation was explained to us. Next we visited sites suggested for a greenhouse and poultry run and we gave provisional approval to such sites and to the cutting down of three trees, which are of no value and which would obstruct the light required for the greenhouse.

Further on we saw at work the Incinerator, which seemed to be quite satisfactory, and we decided to ask the Rural District Council to fence in the dip in the field mentioned at a Board Meeting some time back as a suitable place for disposing of ashes.

We saw the cricket and football field and agreed that awkward depressions might be filled in subject to Mr Thompson's approval and subject also to the removal and replacement of soil and turf.

From the grounds we went to the Court Yard and inspected the men's quarters. Very considerable improvement has been made here; the arrangements seemed to be extremely good and the whole place is very creditable to the Committee and to the men themselves.

Instead of the 50 or more men attending the Summer Camp, in the Winter there are about a dozen men at a time working there under the auspices of the 'Unemployed' Committee. In the Winter the parties stay at Derwent Hall for at least three months; they are married men and they visit their homes once a fortnight. The men attending the Summer Camp are unmarried men and their stay is a three weeks stay.

The men at the Hall now are being trained in market and general gardening and in the keeping of poultry and bees. They are under a supervisor, who is a married man, but is at present living in the men's quarters. All the parties were anxious that some arrangement might be made for the supervisor's wife to join him, but this can be done only by accommodating them in the Hall itself, which brings us to the suggested re-arrangement of the respective holdings by the Hostels Association and the 'Unemployed' Committee.

We went into the Hall and had pointed out to us the gun room, coal cellar and lamp room on the ground floor and two bedrooms above. At present these are in the occupation of the Hostels Association and the suggestion was that they should be transferred to the 'Unemployed' Committee and partitioned off for the use of the before-mentioned Supervisor of the 'small-holding' scheme and his wife. To enable this to be done a staircase from the gun room to the first floor is necessary, but the 'Unemployed' Committee will do this work to the satisfaction of the Board's Engineer.

In place of the gun room, which has been used by the Youth Hostels Association as a drying room, it is proposed that the Association shall have added to their tenancy the butler's pantry. The safe which was in the pantry has been removed to the Offices of the Board, the fronts of the cupboards can be used for partitioning and the 'Unemployed' Committee undertook the making good of the floor.

The Members of the Board were informed that at busy times the Youth Hostels Association require rather more accommodation than they have got. Since Derwent Hall was opened as a Youth Hostel in June, 1932, nearly 8,000 people have stayed there. There is a room, which has been decorated and fitted by the Association, which is used as a Common Room, but on occasion there is need for another room and it was suggested that there should be let to the Youth Hostels Association the Drawing Room. This room and the room used as a Sitting Room by Mr Seery, the Youth Hostels Association Warden, are the only rooms on the ground floor still panelled. The new room will be used by the Youth Hostels Association, and occasionally, by friendly arrangement, by the 'Unemployed' Committee, only on special occasions, for special purposes, as a quiet room, as a relief for the Common Room and for the entertainment of visitors.

We could not see that there was any risk in agreeing to the suggestion and, indeed, the evident care and respect in the use of the Hall by all parties is extremely creditable and extremely pleasing. Lastly, so far as the Youth Hostels Association are concerned, it was arranged that they should have the use of the lavatory on the first floor on the Common Room side and that the Board would re-connect the water supply to this lavatory which had been cut off, owing to a burst pipe, some time back.

Turning again to the 'Unemployed' Committee, we visited the Chapel and ascertained that it has now been de-consecrated, so that there is no objection to the Committee having the use of this building. The Committee will re-glaze the windows, the original glass having been removed when Viscount Fitzalan vacated the Hall. The division of the premises between occupied and unoccupied portions, and between the respective occupied portions, was explained and the proposals appeared to be quite satisfactory.

There seems to be no reason why the Agreement with the Sheffield Allotments and Social Centres for the Unemployed shall not now be completed under the revised arrangements and probably, so far as the Youth Hostels Association are concerned, the matter can be put in order by an endorsement on the existing Agreement.

Having regard to the lapse of time before I could make any formal Report to the Board on the revision of arrangements, and to the fact that he principal points relating to the use of the Hall, etc, by the two Social Service bodies have already been approved, permission has been given for the Youth Hostels Association and the 'Unemployed' Committee to proceed with certain of the arrangements I have already mentioned and I trust that the Members of the Board will agree this was right.

It is not proposed to ask the Youth Hostel Association to pay anything more than the present rent (£52.10s.0d. per annum) or to ask the Sheffield Allotment and Social Centres for the Unemployed to pay any rent at all.

I remain,
Yours sincerely,
(Signed) Hy. H. Bemrose

For a time the Hall closed as a Youth Hostel and in 1939 the Sister Superior of the Notre Dame High School in Sheffield wrote asking the Board if the school could evacuate its scholars to Derwent Hall until the Board required to demolish it in connection with their work. The Board allowed Notre Dame School the use of the Hall after an agreement with the Youth Hostels Association.

The school was also allowed to use the Catholic private chapel, but by this time the hall was rather run down and neglected with suspected dry rot in many areas. It was plainly not ideal to be used as a boarding school, but by late August, the nuns and their maids had cleaned and prepared Derwent Hall for the children. Saturday 1 September saw the first 30 children arrive. These were soon followed by 115 more, which at that time was around one-third of the school roll. Although there was a shortage of everything at the outset, things slowly began to improve. Most welcome was the new Ideal boiler and four bathing cubicles which helped take the edge off the intense cold and miserable surroundings. Jean Pennington, now living in Derby, was a pupil there and hated every minute of it!! She ran away twice and said, 'the whole place was musty and damp, even clothes sometimes had mildew on them. All I can remember was the cold, feeling unhappy and little else'.

As air raid warning systems at the school's Sheffield premises improved, it was hoped that by the summer of 1940 the children could return, but sadly this was not the case. This was just as well because two German bombs fell in the garden of the school's Cavendish Street, Sheffield, premises, shattering all the windows.

Appeals to the Water Board about the poor state of their accommodation yielded sympathy, but little else. Many local people, however, took pity on the children and a supply of fresh vegetable and eggs did help to make life a little more pleasurable. By July 1941 the Board of Education inspector declared the area used by the school at the Hall derelict and living accommodation totally abysmal. On 31 July 1941 the school finally vacated Derwent Hall, and it was then re-opened as a Youth Hostel, with a reasonable number of beds held in reserve for accommodating workmen who were employed on the construction of Ladybower Reservoir.

Derwent Hall at that time also became a social centre for the unemployed, who took over the private chapel, and remained for eight months.

By September 1942, the Water Board had repossessed the Hall and were open to offers for items. Derby Corporation bought 902 square feet of oak panelling for 2s.6d. a square foot, along with the oak flooring from the drawing room for £40. Capn Fitzalan Howard purchased the stone steps leading up to the main entrance for £10 and the iron gates for £7.

The Youth Hostels Association wished to buy the special fireplace from the Drawing Room, but the Board decided to keep it. In its place they said the Youth Hostels Association could have as a memento without payment, the stone effigy, known as Peeping Tom from his place on the stable wall of the Hall. There was a hope that two American businessmen would buy the Hall and rebuild it elsewhere, but this never materialised, so it was left to Mr Charles Boot of Henry Boot & Sons Ltd, to demolish it, for which privilege he paid £800, taking any items he could use or sell.

By the summer of 1943, Mr Boot's men had done their job. Gone forever was the magnificent old mansion, which, over the years, had

seen many changes and comings and goings. One eyewitness recalled looking over the ruins for the last time. *'As the evening sunlight played on the piles of rubble and dressed stone, one still felt there was an air of grandeur about the place. It still looked magnificent, even in ruins.'*

Close to the main gates of Derwent Hall, spanning the River Derwent, stood the pack-horse bridge. When Henry Balguy built his Hall he had rebuilt the bridge on the site of an earlier bridge – by then in a very poor state – which carried the ancient bridle track from Derwent to Glossop. The Water Board planned to demolish the bridge, but it was scheduled under the Ancient Monuments Act (1931) as a monument, the preservation of which was of considered to be of national importance. The Board was asked to dismantle and re-erect the bridge at a site just below Elmin Pitts Farm, as under section 17 of the Derwent Valley Water Act of 1920 they were compelled to provide a footbridge there.

This the Board declined to do. A letter from the Secretary of the Sheffield and Peak District Branch of the Council for the Preservation of Rural England stated that the cost of removal and re-erection of the bridge had been estimated by the architect of the Ancient Monuments Department of HM Office of Works at approximately £1,000. He asked the Board for a substantial contribution towards the cost when the subscription list was opened. The Board contributed £50 with an undertaking that the work must be carried out satisfactorily.

The pack-horse bridge was removed stone by stone, each one being numbered before being put into storage until the money was raised to rebuild it. The bridge now stands at the head of Howden Reservoir at Slippery Stones, as a memorial to John Derry, who did so much to acquaint people with the lesser-known bridges and bridle paths of Derbyshire. If you are in the area it is well worth the walk from Kings Tree to Slippery Stones (just over one mile) to have a look at the old pack-horse bridge.

Derwent Hall stands as a glorious ruin, after demolition began in 1943. The remains of the private chapel, built at a cost of £23,000 in the 1800s, can still be seen on the right. The foundations of these ruins re-appeared in 1959 and 1976 when the dam waters fell abnormally low, and then again in 1989.

Derwent Church was built in 1867 and dedicated to the Saints John and James. The Bingham children, whose father ran the village Post Office, are photographed at the church gates around 1910.

Derwent Church

ONE OF THE most tragic losses at Derwent was the village church, dedicated to the Saints John and James. As with all village churches, it was the centre of social as well as religious activities.

As people in those days rarely moved far from their villages, it was for most Derwent people a case of from font to the grave. Although the church dated only from 1867, the Derwent Valley has a long history of religious worship.

Early records show the acquisition of land in the valley of the River Derwent by the Abbey of Welbeck, by a gift of King John when he was the Duke of Montaigne. It was described as a large territory in the Peak Forest, the pastures of Crookhill, the woods of the Ashop up to Lockerbrook, and from thence up the valley to Derwenthead. The grant of this land was later confirmed by Henry III.

The Lords of Hathersage held land in the Derwent Valley, and on the death of Matthew de Hathersage in 1271 the estate was divided between his co-heiresses, Matilda and Cecilia. Matilda married Sir Walter de Goushill and the couple had two sons, John and Simon. Cecilia married Nigel de Langford and they had a son Nigell and a grandson Oliver. Simon de Goushill and Oliver de Langford gave their lands to the Abbey of Welbeck.

On part of the new land, the monks built an extensive farm known as Abbey Grange. A taxation roll in 1299 valued the Welbeck estate at Crookhill at £7.17s.6d. and the tithe 15s.9d. Granges such as the one in the Derwent Valley were the source of immense wealth to the Abbey,

Derwent's Anglican church was at the centre of the village's social as well as religious activities.

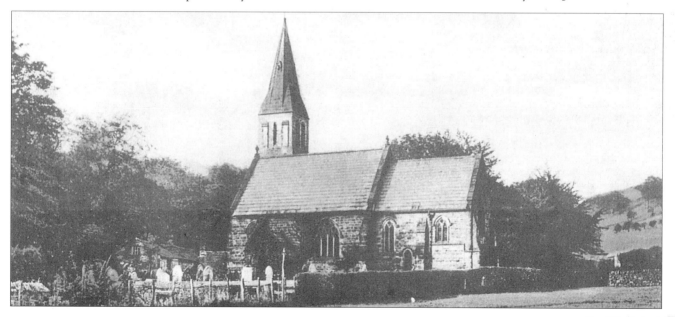

and careful breeding and good management gave them large herds of cattle, sheep and swine. In the reign of Edward III the Grange obtained an exemption by the authority of the Pope from the payment of tithes. In the fields they grew cereals, vegetables in their gardens, and orchards full of fruit.

The White Cannons were known for their abstinence, deep piety and graceful dress – a long white cloak and hood over a white cassock with a small white cap. For many years the monks were vegetarians, but as meat became plentiful, the habits of a lifetime changed. The monks also built no less than four chapels in and around the valley.

The first chapel was attached to the Grange itself, and the second stood in the Derwent woodlands close to the site of the old church of Derwent, where there was built a corn mill. This chapel was probably the most important, being close to the mill and water, and a small hamlet soon sprung up around it. A third chapel stood on a site between Marebottom and Birchinlee, and many old maps show a Chapel Lane in that area, bearing out the tradition.

The third and fourth chapels – the fourth used to stand in the woodlands close to the old Roman road, about 130 yards south of Hope Cross – were Wayfarer chapels, offering travellers both religious sustenance and food and shelter for the night. If they stayed longer, travellers were given tasks to do to pay for their keep.

The monks never missed an opportunity to gather acorns from the woods, and from herbs they made many fine concoctions and potions. In 1285 the Abbot of Welbeck was fined £20 for damage to the King's woods in the Derwent and Ashop Valleys. Later the monks were granted a charter for the rights of herbage and foliage in certain parts of the Derwent Valley. Not only were they good at farming, but the monks were good bridge builders too, building one bridge opposite the Grange and another lower down the valley on the site of the later pack-horse bridge close to Derwent Hall.

They continued their happy and prosperous ways until the dissolution of monasteries and abbeys in the reign of King Henry VIII. The Reformation made Henry much richer but turned many of the monks into homeless wanderers.

One by one the chapels around Derwent began to deteriorate, until only one remained as a place of, by then Protestant, religious worship. It continued thus until 1757. In 1688, the Earl of Devonshire owned the corn mill at Derwent and pastured sheep at Derwent Woodlands. He paid, through his agent, Mr Greaves of Rowlee, a gratuity of five pounds to the Revd Mr Nicholls for his services at Derwent Chapel, which had become a chapel-of-ease to the Parish of Hathersage. When the old chapel was pulled down, it made way for a smaller second chapel in 1757, said to have been an ugly building with a square bell tower, containing one bell, with below it a large round-headed window at the west end. After this second chapel was removed in 1867, the church so many people still remember was built. As they were pulling down the 1757 chapel, fragments of the fourteenth century building were found embedded in the masonry, including mouldings, pillars, capitols and window sills. These were used on the building of the 1867 church.

Derwent Church was an excellently proportioned building, consisting of chapel, nave, porch, and north aisle with an arcade of three

arches. A western tower and spire were added in 1873. The church was consecrated on 18 August 1869. In the churchyard near the south entrance stood a sundial, the work of Daniel Rose, clerk of Derwent in the eighteenth century. The register of baptisms dated back to 1813, marriage and burials from 1869. Other notable items housed in the church included an ancient stone font, dated 1670, which had been rescued from the Hall gardens, where it had been used as a flower pot in earlier times. There was also a silver paten dated 1763 and inscribed Chapel of Derwent, from Dr Denman.

The patronage of the earlier chapel had been sold by Mr Balguy to Joseph Denman MD about that time. Joseph Denman was the father of the first Lord Denman. The Derwent chalice of Elizabethan origin was made in London in 1584, and has engraved on it figures, symbolic of the elements.

In 1937, when the building of Ladybower Dam was imminent, the Water Board bought the church, churchyard and vicarage at a cost of £18,244.13s., and then rented back the church and churchyard at an annual rent of £120. The vicarage rent was set at £30 per annum.

One of the biggest problems for the Water Board was the churchyard, as 284 bodies were buried there. Under Section 17 of the Water Act of 1920 the Water Board was responsible for both the removal of the human remains from Derwent Churchyard, and their re-interment in consecrated ground in which burials may legally take place, subject to the approval of the Bishop of Derby. As there was not enough ground spare at Bamford Churchyard, the Water Board

Derwent Church consisted of a chapel, nave, porch, north aisle with an arcade of three arches, plus a western tower and spire. Fragments of masonary from a fourteenth century church built on the same site, including mouldings, pillars, capitals and window sills were incorporated into the newer building.

In 1940, behind tarpaulin screens, human remains were exhumed from the graveyard. They were re-interred in Bamford Churchyard – the Derwent Valley Water Board having paid £500 towards the cost of extending it for ths purpose.

decided to appropriate a piece of their own land close to Moorland Road at Yorkshire Bridge for the purpose of a burial ground.

The Bishop of Derby visited the site and approved it, subject to the Board fencing in the land, making approach roads and agreeing to keep the burial ground in order in perpetuity. All was agreed, and the problem seemed to have been solved, until it was pointed out that under the Burials Act no new burial ground can be made within one hundred yards of a dwelling-house without the consent in writing of the owner or occupier of such a dwellinghouse. Only one house, known as Bamford Lodge, and owned by Mr G.R. Wilson, was within one hundred yards of the proposed burial ground, and Mr

Wilson objected so strongly to the burial ground that the plan had to be scrapped.

At one stage the idea of capping the graves and leaving the bodies in place at Derwent was suggested, but then the Vicar of Bamford approached the Water Board asking if they would contribute to the cost of extending the Bamford Churchyard. This the Water Board agreed to do, on condition that the human remains from Derwent could be buried there. The Water Board paid £500 towards the cost, and when the extension was complete, the Bishop of Derby consecrated the ground on Saturday 8 October, 1938.

By December 1938, the Water Board had applied to the Ministry of Health with a view to obtaining an Order of the Privy Council closing Derwent Churchyard for burials.

Records of each grave opened had to be kept, and a sketch made of each grave-stone or monument. The condition of the coffin and remains were logged, as were the time and date of exhumation and re-interment. The whole task was carried out under the supervision of the Derbyshire County Medical Officer of Health, who wrote to the Water Board on 4 July 1940 stating that the removal of the remains had been carried out to his entire satisfaction.

The last service held in Derwent Church was on 17 March 1943, and was attended by the Bishop of Derby and members of the Water Board. In his final address to the congregation the Bishop said, 'We build churches with the idea that they will endure forever, but we know in our hearts that our buildings will not endure, for we have seen so much destruction during the war that we no longer have the illusion of permanence of the work of human hands'.

The person hardest hit by the flooding must have been the Vicar of Derwent, the late Walter

E. Rouse, for he had been priest there for more than forty-five years. He had been the Board's chaplain to the workpeople when Derwent and Howden Dams were constructed, and on retiring in 1943 he was allowed to continue to live in the vicarage, at £20 per annum rent. He died in 1945 at the age of 81. After his death, the Water Board decided to pull down the vicarage.

After the last service in Derwent Church, the Water Board took possession of the church and prepared to demolish it. It had been hoped that the church could have been rebuilt on a new site, but this proved impractical, so it was decided to transfer the endowments of Derwent Church to Frecheville, to the south of Sheffield, which at that time had only a temporary church. As there was about £12,000 attached to the Derwent living, the Bishop decided that the sum could be most usefully devoted to erecting a parish church at Frecheville, now dedicated to St Cyprian.

The silver paten and the Derwent Chalice are now both housed at Frecheville. The ancient font, after a spell lost, is now restored to former glory in Tansley Church near Matlock. The four bells from Derwent now ring out calling the

From the pulpit of Derwent Church, the Bishop of Derby addressed a packed congregation at the last service on 17 March 1943. Villagers, hikers and Water Board members were in attendance. The churchyard outside was by then empty and overgrown, the graves and their contents long since removed to Bamford.

With its treasures removed, Derwent Church was quickly demolished though the spire remained until 1947. In the distance still stand cottages. The one on the right had been the Post Office.

people of Chelmorton, near Buxton, together, and the East Window – a copy of an old master – can be seen in Hathersage Church.

The Church fabric was in excellent condition. The pulpit was the work of a master craftsman, and at the back of the altar stood an oak panel once housed in Winchester Cathedral. All these found new and grateful homes. After all the items had been removed, demolition was quickly carried out. The Water Board decided at first to leave the church spire standing as a memorial to the people of Derwent, but as time went on they came to regret this decision.

Also to perish was the school and schoolhouse, for which the Water Board paid £1,000. All the teachers at Derwent School were female, and were

capable when needed of disciplining any of the children who stepped out of line. For some of those children it meant getting up very early and arriving home late to achieve their long walk to attend Derwent School. Lunchtime for some was a cup of warm water and little else. By the time it came to go home the tummy over-ruled the brain, and Mr Colin Elliott remembers one group of children on their journey home to Ashopton, stopping off in one of the fields belonging to Grainfoot farm to remove a turnip to make the journey home a little more pleasurable. All was forgotten until the next morning when they arrived at school to find the farmer talking to the headmistress in the school yard. The cane was administered later that morning but one of the recipients recalled the punishment was hard to take, but the turnip tasted so sweet it was worth all the pain!

On cold winter mornings the warming glow from the cast-iron stove helped to dry clothes and thaw out young bones, but in summer time many lessons were conducted out in the open by the side of the River Derwent which ran close by the school. To help with reading and learning the alphabet, at work times, a large flat stone carved with the alphabet was used. This was donated by the local farmer who had it carved to help his son with his reading at home as he had fallen behind at school.

During the 1995 drought I received a phone call from a former scholar at Derwent who related the story of the alphabet stone and its whereabouts today. With the aid of his instructions I was eventually able to locate the old alphabet stone, still where he had last placed it in 1943. After inspecting the stone as instructed I replaced it back in its resting place and there it still remains today. I was saddened that other people could not enjoy seeing the stone but I was so grateful to have been allowed to view a little piece of valley history. Miss H. Bingham, one of the teachers at Derwent, moved on to teach at Bamford School and not only was she excellent, but liked by everyone she taught.

Also noteworthy was Mill Cottage, a delightful house from which Mrs H. Thorpe served many a rambler with tea. Had Mrs Thorpe lived she would have seen her third home perish beneath the impounded waters of the Derwent Valley, for her first home at Ronksley Farm had been submerged under Howden Dam, whilst her second – Hancock's Farm – lay under the waters of the Derwent Dam. But Mrs Thorpe died before her home was needed.

Gone also is Bridge End Farm, a 300-year-old farmhouse that had been the home of Mr A. Shephard for more than fifty years. The old farmhouse held an ale licence in earlier times, receiving regular supplies from local brewers in Hathersage.

By the late autumn of 1943, Derwent was little more than piles of rubble. Its inhabitants had moved on to rebuild their lives elsewhere. Many settled on the Water Board's purpose-built housing estate at Yorkshire Bridge, about 3½ miles away, whilst others travelled to many corners of the High Peak.

Lower down the valley, at Ladybower, the outlet valves were being closed, and soon the impounded river waters were covering the ruins of Derwent. Only one landmark was left to bear witness to the village, a stark church spire standing alone in the cold murky waters of Ladybower Reservoir. But even that did not last long, for it was blown up, alleged for safety reasons, on 15 December 1947.

A rare photograph of the ruined interior of Derwent Church.

The church spire stands as a stark reminder above the cold murky waters. By December 1947, this too had been demolished.

The Story of Tip

THERE ARE MANY LEGENDS surrounding animals and their bravery and devotion. The story of Tip, an 11-year-old sheep-dog bitch, bred and owned by local shepherd, Mr Joseph Tagg, then of Yorkshire Bridge, is thought to be unequalled in a dog's devotion to its master.

On Saturday 12 December 1953, Mr Tagg set off with Tip for the Upper Derwent Valley to attend some sheep. Hours later, when they failed to return home, the alarm was raised and an RAF mountain rescue unit joined by shepherds and gamekeepers commenced a widespread search of the hills and the valley, but failed to find any sign of them.

At weekends, hundreds of ramblers joined family and friends covering hundreds of miles, but still no sign or trace of either Mr Tagg or Tip were found. Many searches had to be abandoned due to the snow, as it was particularly bad that winter.

On Saturday 27 March 1954, Mr Sam Bingham, who accompanied by Mr Joe Shepherd were rounding up sheep high on the Ronksley moors when Mr Bingham noticed what he thought was an old coat laid in a dip. As he approached he realised it was Tip, who was only a few feet away from the dead body of her 86-year-old master. Tip gave Mr Bingham a feeble wag of her tail, and he had a major problem getting the dog away as she didn't want to end her long vigil. She was very weak, wet and thin, and had to be carried down from the moors to Mr Bingham's transport.

Soon Tip was at home and making a good recovery with Mr Tagg's niece, Miss Thorp. How Tip survived the 15-week vigil is not fully known, but Mr Bingham thought she must have lived on dead rabbits and birds killed by the severe winter. Tip was later awarded a canine bravery medal, equal to the dog's VC, and continued a very happy life for a further 18 months.

Mr Tagg was one of the area's most famous shepherds and lived in the Derwent Valley all his life. He was for many years the shepherd to the Duke of Norfolk at Derwent Hall and a founder member of the local sheep-dog trials in 1905. He was one of the finest sheep-dog breeders to be found and sold dogs at home and in the United States. He cannot have bred one finer than his 'Tip'. A memorial raised by public subscription stands just above the Derwent dam wall (west side) a fitting tribute to man's best friend. Tip's final resting place is a beautiful site on Derwent Edge, overlooking the Valley.

Ashopton Village

AFTER THE ROMANS left Britain, the roads they had built were allowed to fall into disrepair. By the Middle Ages they were little more than rutted tracks, but around 1770, following the Turnpike Road Act of that year, roads slowly began to improve, with engineers like McAdam and Telford introducing new methods of road laying. It was these new, surfaced roads that brought about the great coaching era, which reached its peak around 1820.

When the Sheffield to Glossop turnpike road was built in 1821, Ashopton grew and developed as traffic increased on the road, for travel by coach

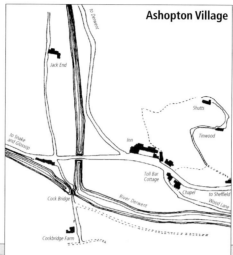

Ashopton village pictured around 1900, with the Ashopton Inn in the centre.

and horse became popular. But coach travel in those far-off days was exacting of both horses and the human frame. More and more coaching stops were needed, for they not only provided a welcome break on a long journey, but food, warmth and shelter for man and beast alike. The *Ashopton Inn* was built as one such stop in 1824, to provide a welcome pause before the long haul up the Snake Valley to Glossop. Standing at the Derwent road junction of the Sheffield to Glossop road, this ivy-clad old building changed little over the years, retaining all the warmth and charm one would expect of a late Georgian coaching inn.

The first landlord of the *Ashopton Inn* was William Askew, whose family were horse-breeders and dealers from Tideswell. On 18

September 1925, the Water Board also owned the *Yorkshire Bridge Inn* and the *Ladybower Inn*, and they did look into the idea of rebuilding the *Ashopton Inn* on a new site, retaining the old licence, but as it involved complicated factors the idea was dropped. On 7 January 1943, the Licensing Justices at Chapel-en-le-Frith transferred the licence of the *Ashopton Inn* to premises at New Mills under the Walker and Hornfray Brewery, with the brewery paying £500 for the said licence. On 28 January 1943, the Water Board terminated Mrs C.M. Bradwell's lease and took possession of the *Ashopton Inn*, agreeing to make her an ex-gratia payment of £500 in full settlement of all claims. Within a month, the old coaching inn was in ruins.

Looking north across Ashopton, with the Ashopton Inn on the left at one end of the village and the chapel at the other. The building on the hillside is Tinwood Farm.

Looking towards Sheffield, the upper photograph of Toll Bar Cottage, probably taken in the 1920s, shows Mrs Dakin's shop and tearoom.

The village became a popular coaching stop in the 19th century, and was equally popular with hikers well into the 20th, as this group photograph taken outside the Ashopton Inn *demonstrates.*

At the Bamford junction of the Sheffield to Glossop road, at the corner of Wood Lane, a few yards short of the *Ashopton Inn*, on the opposite side of the road, stood the old toll-bar cottage. The date 1821 was carved over the doorway. For almost four years it stood on the opposite side of the road and some 80 yards further up Wood Lane, but in 1825 the Turnpike Trust had decided this position was unworkable and rebuilt it on the new site. As the sidebar dealt with people entering from Bamford, travellers along the Sheffield to Glossop road had to contend with the main bar.

All the tolls taken at Ashopton had to be paid into the Toll Trust Office in Paradise Square, Sheffield, with the keeper having to walk there and back – a long, dangerous trip, usually taking three hours each way.

The last toll was taken at Ashopton on 16 September 1875 by the assistant keeper, Mr Eber Marshall, after which date the toll-bar was given up, and the house sold. The Turnpike Trust had expired and the road became free of tolls.

In 1935 the Water Board paid £1,100 for the toll-bar cottage and sales shop, along with three acres of land, and on 16 September 1942, the cottage was pulled down.

Ashopton village housed one of the finest Methodist Chapels to be seen in the High Peak. Built in 1840, the chapel was enlarged in 1896, with the older part of the building used for the Sunday School and public meetings. Before the chapel was built, earlier prayer meetings were held in local farms, usually once a fortnight, with many guest preachers travelling miles to attend the meetings. During the bad winter

A sumptuous Harvest Festival at Ashopton Methodist Chapel in the late 1930s. By the summer of 1943 this splendid chapel was no more.

Bachelor's Tea Ashopton

months, local people had frequently to stand in, and John Longden was one such famous local Woodlands preacher. He was also the innkeeper of the *Snake Inn*, higher up the valley, and many of the prayer meetings were held at the inn.

Each year, about Springtime, concerts were held in the chapel. These were known locally as the Bachelor Parties, for young men in the area produced the shows and provided the refreshments for the many local people who turned out to enjoy these really entertaining evenings.

On 22 December 1938, the last marriage service was performed at the chapel, on a day which began with a heavy snowfall. All the vil-lagers turned out to sweep a path to Ashopton Chapel, where the Revd Simpson joined together Miss Olive Ollerenshaw and Frank Booth. Olive wore a dress of rust velvet, whilst her bridesmaid – her sister, Beattie – was in bottle green. The organ was played by her brother, Willis, and the groom's best man was Harold Bailey. Despite the inclement weather, the newly-weds honeymooned in Blackpool!

In November 1936, the Water Board had agreed to pay £2,800 for Ashopton Chapel, with completion of the sale being deferred until they took possession. As people were already moving away from the area, it was decided to hold the

Regular 'Bachelors Parties' were held in Ashopton Chapel, when the entertainment was provided by the single men of the village. Every woman wears a hat in this picture, taken around 1910.

last service on 25 September 1939, and this was conducted by the Revd J. Atkinson. The final hymn sung was *The Day is Dying in the West*. From then until its destruction in 1943, the chapel was used as a depot for the local Home Guard.

Although part of the fine stained-glass window from the chapel was transferred to Hope Chapel Sunday School, by the summer of 1943 the Chapel was no more. Another part of High Peak history lay in ruins.

Also to perish was Cockbridge Farm, built around 1838 and thought to be the third house built on the same site. It had been the home for three generations of the Thorp family. Aaron, the last in line, wrote to the Water Board on 25 March 1937 asking to be released from his tenancy of the farm. He then moved from the district to Ashbourne. Cockbridge Farm then

This stone-built bridge crossed the River Derwent to the west of Ashopton.

Right, Jack End Farm, slightly to the north of Ashopton. The pillars of Ashopton viaduct now stand almost in the old farm yard.

In the early 1940s the huge steel and concrete viaduct was built across the bottom of the Derwent valley. White lines and kerb markings tell us that this is wartime.

became a guest house, the shippan being turned into workmen's lodging rooms.

On 1 March 1937, the Water Board purchased Jack End Farm, and gave the tenant, Mr T. Bridge, notice to quit, as they required the land for roads, viaducts and pipelines. One of the Ashopton viaduct pillars now stands almost in the old farmyard, for the new section of the Sheffield to Glossop road was built well to the north of the old (now submerged) road.

By the summer of 1943 Ashopton was no more. The inn, tollbar cottage and chapel were reduced to rubble. Shops, farms and cottages (one used to be an alehouse known as the *Highland Laddie*) were all laid low, and above the ruins there now towered a giant viaduct which carried the diverted Sheffield to Glossop road – now the A57. As the impounded waters of Ladybower began to rise up the mighty pillars, so did the ruins of Ashopton Village disappear for all time, leaving no memorials and no landmarks, just memories.

Ruins

At low water the old railway gantry pillars which carried the track to Howden can still be seen in Derwent Reservoir, almost one hundred years after it was built.

AS THE YEARS PASS, the legend of the lost villages of Derwent and Ashopton lives on. Thousands of people visit the Upper Derwent Valley each year and marvel at the scenic beauty of this part man-made lakeland. Many still remember the valley as it was before the waters came, and if you ask them to compare the valley now with the valley as it was, they generally claim that it is hard to choose. But their eyes tell a different story, and often a smile comes across their faces as they speak of the old days, when the River Derwent was little more than a babbling brook, when one could stay the night at Derwent Hall and it would not cost the earth, or how pleasant it was, after a day spent walking in the hills, to rest with a drink and a meal at the old inn at Ashopton. Memories, fine memories.

Several times since 1943, in times of extreme drought, the ruins of the village of Derwent have re-appeared, whereas Ashopton, further down the valley, has never been seen, save through the occasional diver's face mask, and into the cold murky water, to see only fleeting glimpses of piles of rubble and stone that were once a family home.

Derwent ruins, however, have re-appeared on occasions from 1947 onwards, allowing hundreds of visitors to once again stand on Vicarage Lane, walk up the old church path and stand on the massive area of stonework that was once Derwent Hall. Many have removed stones, taken as souvenirs, whilst others have found interesting artefacts dating back to earlier times. One item found in 1989 was the cricket scoreboard markers, wrapped in an oil-based cloth with the numbers 1943 inside.

Another piece of history re-appeared in 1988 when contractors were refurbishing Bamford filtration plant. Hidden in long grass and brambles was a large stone bearing a coat of arms with three diamond shapes on it and the date 1672. It was later found to be the lintel stone which stood over the main doorway of Derwent Hall, removed in 1943 and taken to Bamford for storage, before being handed back to the descendants of the Balguy family who built the original hall. But it was never collected and now has returned home, sited in the garden of Saint Henry's, now the village hall at Derwent.

Again, in 1989 two explorers were excavating a small building to the right of the old vicarage when they found a large iron ring cast into a stone floor. Buried a little deeper they found an old pick shaft with a leather hand grip. Where they were digging was later discovered to be the site location of the vicarage pigsty. Walter Rouse, the old vicar, used to keep one pig, but when the time came for porky to depart from this world, the vicar would not be around to see it as he hated to see blood

spilt. The ring was used to chain up the pig and the pick shaft used to soften the blow of having its throat cut!

Many visitors are surprised how little there is left of the old church and spire at Derwent. This is explained by the fact that in 1959 during the drought of that year, the Derwent Valley Water Board removed much of the church stone from the site and used it as beaching around Ladybower reservoir. Much of it can still be seen

Over the years the Derwent ruins have re-appeared on several occasions.

in the Mill Brook area. The large date stone (1867) remains on the site, as does the church path and gate posts. One building many visitors mistake for the church is the old Derwent Valley Water Board valve house, the only complete building on the ruined site. Its replacement now stands on the west bank near Bridge End car park.

The ruins of Bridge End Farm stand on the west side of the valley marked by two stone troughs and a gatepost. The small stone trough was used for the family's drinking water, and the larger one that stood near the cowshed was used by the farm animals. The main ruin in the village is that of Derwent Hall. Massive amounts of carved stonework remain and it is marked by a still complete carved stone gatepost, and the old stone corner seat which was used by courting couples, still standing close to the old river bed.

Soon, even in drought conditions, little will be left to see of the old Derwent Village. In the words of a one-time Water Board member reflecting on the loss of the two villages, 'The lines of a picture soften, but they never fade'. So be it.

SILENT VALLEY AT WAR

Vic Hallam tells the story of the six long years of World War II – of the Lancaster Bombers that practiced over the Upper Derwent Valley before the famous Dambusters raids, and of the last years of the lost villages of Ashopton and Derwent.

Available from Sheaf Publishing, 191 Upper Allen Street, Sheffield S3 7GW, price £5.50 per copy (includes p&p).

Author's Acknowledgements

I wish to thank all those who have supported and encouraged me over the years, and helped keep alive the history of this small corner of England. I hope you have enjoyed looking back with me over the Silent Valley! Until next time!!

Also I am grateful in no small way to Mr Colin Elliot, who has allowed me to use many excellent photographs from his private collection and also to the following, who have supplied photographs or helped in producing this and earlier editions: Sheffield Newspapers; *The Derbyshire Times*; Local Studies, Sheffield Central Library; The Hunter Archaeological Society; The Clarion Ramblers' Association; Mr W. A. Poucher; Mr P. Fletcher; Mr W. Conduit; Mr Richard Heath; Mr & Mrs Frank Booth; Mrs A. Frost; Mr M. L. Murphy; Mr J. Newton; Mr M. Needham; and Mr R. Filiman. As far as possible I have tried to acknowledge help or photographs, but apologise if anyone has been overlooked!

This book is dedicated to the memory of the late Joe Frost, a sadly missed friend and brother-in-law. *Vic Hallam*